little LEENA learns about Ramadan

By Zainab Fadlallah

yum..

..yum..

yum..

yum..

Little Leena wakes up from a nap and smells a delicious scent coming from the kitchen.

"Is mummy baking?" She thought.

"I wonder what it could be?"

Could it be cookies?
Cupcakes with sprinkles.

Or maybe it's a chocolate cake!
She decides to go and have a look.

On her way she starts to sing "there's a yummy yummy, in my tummy tummy."

Walking into the living room she sees colorful lights and decorations.

Then there it was on the table, a magnificent chocolate cake.

She rushes to the kitchen excitedly and sees her family sitting together sharing a **delicious meal**.

"**Wow**." She whispers and asks "What's going on ?"

"It's **Ramadan**." Her older sister Safiyya answers.

"Ramadan? What is Ramadan?" asks Leena.

"Ramadan is the 9th month in the Lunar calendar." Says Safiyya.

It starts as soon as a new moon is sighted."

"Grown ups fast from when
the sun rises till the sun sets
and if any brave kids wants to
try they are welcome to."

"What is fasting?"
Asks a confused Leena.

"Fasting means
we do not eat or
drink during
daylight hours."
Says Safiyya.

"We do not EAT or DRINK !"
Shrieks Leena.

"Yes." Says Safiyya .

"Not even SNACKS or some JUICE?"
"Not even those." Giggles Safiyya.

"After a long day of fasting we can eat
all kinds of tasty food you can imagine."

"YUMMM..." says Leena
"That sounds lovely."

"What makes Ramadan special?" Leena wonders.

"Ramadan is special because during the month we try to be extra kind and do as many good deeds as we can . Like sharing our toys or helping out a friend ." Says Safiyya.

"We also try to remember to be grateful for all the things we have."

"Look fiyya, presents!" Exclaims Leena.

"Yes, these presents are for Eid day."

"When Ramadan is over, we celebrate the next day by wearing new clothes, visiting our family, friends, and neighbours and also share gifts."

"I love gifts." Says Leena.

"Me too." Says Safiyya.

"I can't wait to celebrate Eid with
all my cousins!" exclaims Leena.

"Do you know what we say to each other during Ramadan?"

"What do we say?" Asks Leena.

"We say Ramadan Mubarak !"

"Which means have a blessed Ramadan."

"Really?" says Leena.
"Let's go and tell everyone!"

Leena and Safiyya run to the kitchen with the biggest smiles on their faces, shouting on the top of their voices

"Ramadan Mubarak!"

The End

Printed in Great Britain
by Amazon